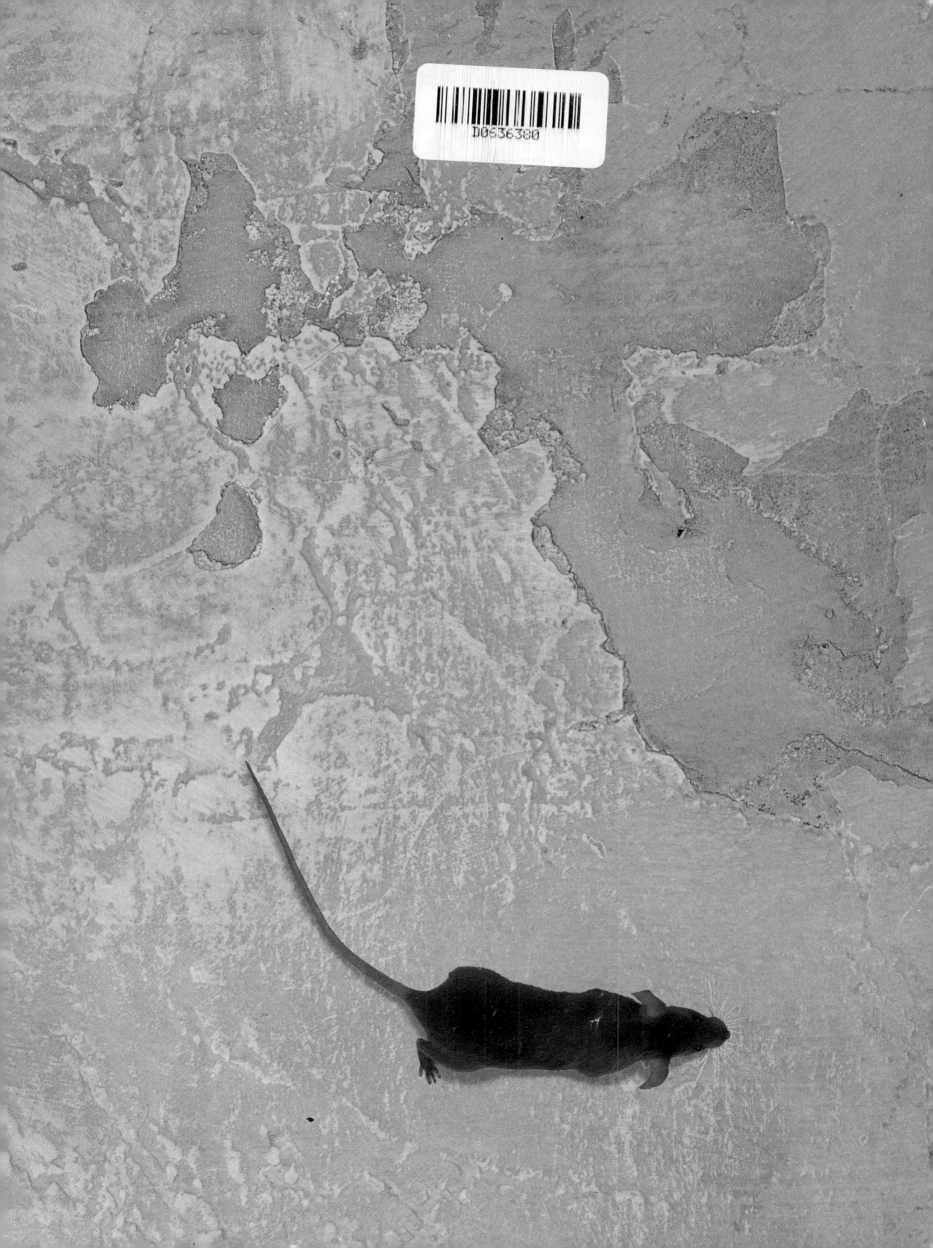

A DORLING KINDERSLEY BOOK

Project editor Miriam Farbey
Art editor Karen Fielding
Designer Mary Sandberg
Stylist Marion McLornan
Photography Tim Ridley
Production Louise Barratt
Photographer's assistant Nick Goodall
Additional photography Dave King, Michael Crockett
Consultant Dennis Severs

Dorling Kindersley would like to thank Borderline, A. D. Carpets, Clifton
Little Venice, Faith Eaton, Carole Handslip, Simon Money, Neal's Yard Dairy,
Pearl Cross Antiques Ltd., Robert Purves, V. V. Rouleaux, and Paul Scannell
for their help in producing this book. Silver supplied by Langfords, in the
London Silver Vaults. Meadow set designed and made by
Rocky Road Productions Limited.

First published in Great Britain in 1995 by Dorling Kindersley Limited,
9 Henrietta Street, London WC2E 8PS

A CIP catalogue record for this book is available from the British Library.

ISBN: 0–7513–5310–8

Colour reproduction by Classic Scan, Singapore
Printed and bound in Italy by L.E.G.O.

🐭 Follow the trail of five green peas in every picture.

🐭 Search carefully for the mice hidden in each scene.

A COUNTRY MOUSE IN THE TOWN HOUSE

by
Henrietta

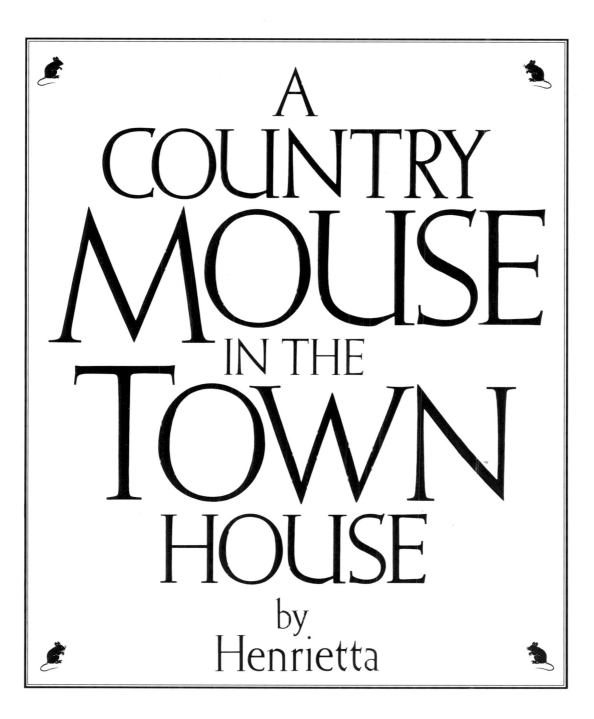

DORLING KINDERSLEY
London • New York • Stuttgart

In a snug country cottage a fat little mouse
Enjoyed, undisturbed, the whole range of the house;
With plain food content, she would breakfast on cheese,
She dined upon berries, and supped on green peas.

A friend from the town to the cottage did write:

"Leave your forests and fields for the city's delights;

Why not come to the town, as quick as you please,

I'll treat you to more than mere berries and peas."

*T*o the town house she came, wriggled under the door;
"Come in!" cried the town mouse. "See what I've in store,
With me shall you feast just as long as you please,
Come, leave those old berries and horrid green peas.

"Here are custard and trifle, and cheesecakes galore,
Nice sweetmeats and jellies, and twenty things more;
Elegant dishes designed just to please,
Far better than berries and boring old peas."

They were merrily munching when into the room
Came the dog and the cat, and the maid with her broom:
The mice in a fright through a small hole did squeeze;
How the country mouse sighed for her berries and peas.

As they fled through the drawing room she cried: "Away!
I can venture no longer in this town to stay;
For if oft you receive interruptions like these,
I would far rather have my plain berries and peas."

own House
London

I can hear something
scratching.
There must be mice
in the house!
I wonder where
they are hiding?

They hid in a room full of toys bright and gay,
But the cat with the mice was more eager to play;
With tightly shut eyes and trembling knees,
The country mouse yearned for sweet berries and peas.

*T*hey scrambled upstairs, scuttled on to a bed:
"Let's make our escape," the country mouse said.
"I want to go home to the flowers and the trees,
And, best of all, berries and lovely green peas.

"*Your* living is splendid and gay to be sure,
But the dread of disturbance you ever endure;
I taste true delight in contentment and ease,
And live happy forever on berries and peas."